The ups & downs of being in your FORTIES

The ups & downs of being in your FORTIES

Tony Husband

ARCTURUS

ARCTURUS

This edition published in 2019 by Arcturus Publishing Limited
26/27 Bickels Yard, 151–153 Bermondsey Street,
London SE1 3HA

ISBN: 978-1-78828-362-5
AD006042UK

Printed in China

INTRODUCTION

Bob Hope said you know you're getting old when the candles cost more than your birthday cake. But being in your 40s isn't old, is it? Of course, you may have to make a few adjustments, like perfecting your comb-over, getting yourself some nice, elasticized slacks and learning to sleep in your socks. Accept it, you're slowly turning into your parents. You're built for comfort not speed now.

In truth, my 40s were golden years. I was employed as a full-time cartoonist, my work was in demand and I was prolific enough to be able to afford a nice house with a big garden ideal for a young family. Trips to London became frequent and life opened up. I joined the Groucho Club in its heyday with all the madness that came with it. My social life expanded to a crazy level as I got to know more and more people. I was living in the land of rock'n'roll, which was perhaps what led *The Times* to call me the Keith Richards of cartooning. I burned the candle at both ends – as well as in the middle – and got away with it. You could back then!

It's harder to be 40 now. There are so many new things to worry about. How do you keep up with the people whose lives seem beyond perfect on Facebook? How can you be cool when you still live with your parents? At what age should you stop wearing jeans? You won't find the answers in this book, but if you recognize the situations and smile, that's good enough for me.

Tony Husband

'It's official, darling: the 40s are the new 30s.'

'Fancy going for a drink?'

'Yes, but does your personal trainer have to be half your age?'

'I'll choose the au pair thank you very much!'

'I've reached the age where I'm ripe for counselling.'

'John, wake up... I'm 43; you're 45:
I've decided we'll become vegans!'

'The thing is I don't feel nearly as old as I thought I would.'

'Now we're in our 40s, isn't it time to look for a static caravan?'

'I found some hair in the shower. It can't be mine.
Please tell me you've been showering the dog again.'

'Have you noticed how, now they've hit their 40s,
we get a lot fewer walks?'

'Do you have anything to invigorate a man of a certain age?'

'I doubt very much your trousers have shrunk, Matt.'

'I don't care whether it's Merlot, Malbec or Mataro
as long as it's strong.'

'Yawning when it's time to buy your round? Ha! You never did that in your 30s.'

'Hi, mate. No, I can't afford to come out for a drink.
It's the "Ex-Factor". I'm broke!'

'Just started my bucket list: by the time I'm 41 I'll have bungee-jumped in New Zealand; by 42 — gone over the Niagara Falls in a barrel; by 43 — swum with dolphins; by 44 —'

'Not so much crow's feet as canary tiptoes. Looking good, girl!'

'Bad news! We can't go on Under-40s holidays any more.'

'I'm joining a gym to tone up.' 'Tell me: are you having an affair?'

'Being too old to rock and roll isn't the end of the world, Roger.'

'14 units of alcohol a week?! I was sure it was per day.'

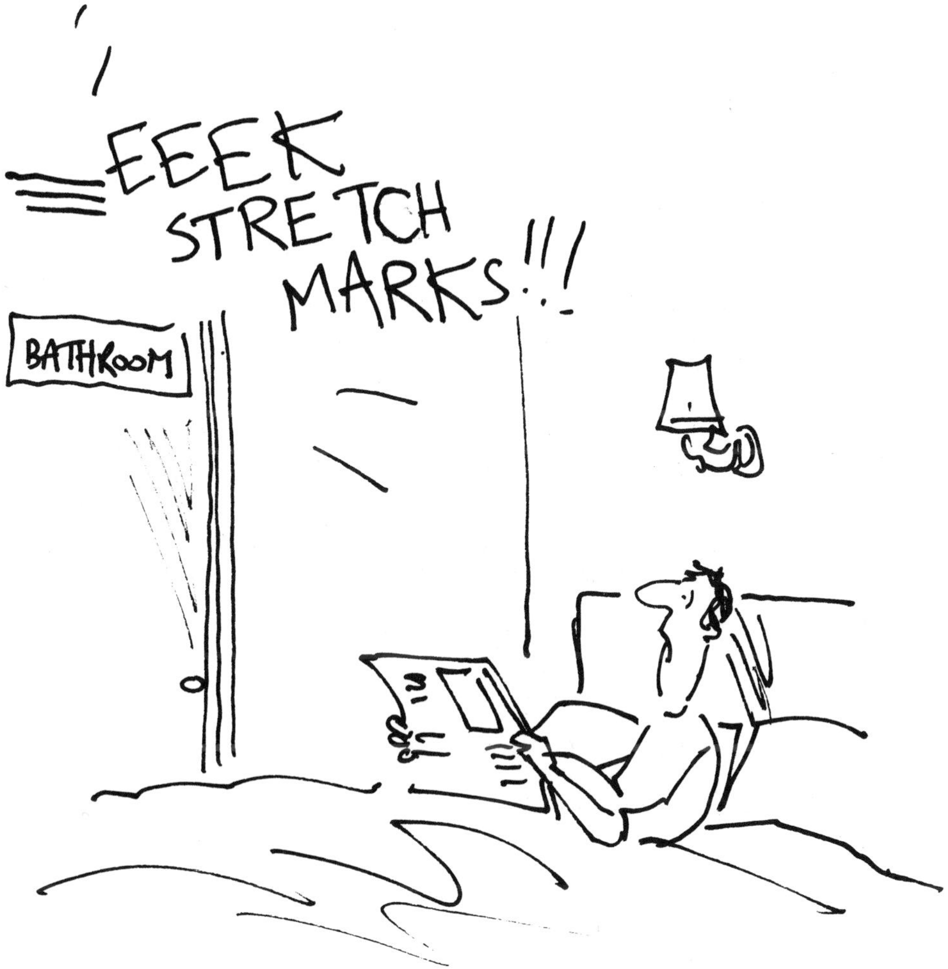
EEEK STRETCH MARKS!!!
BATHROOM

'Son, now you're 45, your mother and I were wondering if you'd ever thought of finding a place of your own?'

'Don't ask me my age. I never use the "F" word.'

'Did you never fancy having children?'

'We've still got another half to go!'

'It's from the wife upstairs in bed: can we keep the noise down?!'

'So long, lads. Thanks for the good times.'

'You're in your 40s?! Wow, cool!'

'Darling, wake up... I've decided I'm going to climb Everest.'

'I'm trying to keep my waist size below my age.'

'We don't talk any more, just text.'

'So we're vegetarian now, are we? Er, since when?'

'You've got absolutely no idea just how serious man flu is.'

'You can't come home, son. Your dad's turned your bedroom into a gym.'

'Scuse me, at what age should a man stop wearing jeans?'

'Sadly, burning the candle at both ends is no longer an option at your age.'

'I've made an executive decision, Ralph:
we ditch the sports car and get a people carrier.'

'I bet my dad's got more tattoos than your dad.'

'Hey, Joe, remember when we played football on Saturday mornings.'

'Is this our future now?'

'I can't remember: is it cooler for guys to date older women
or the other way round?'

'I don't know, perhaps we should be thinking about
a more practical car now.'

'Blimey, when she's 10, you'll be 55... that's ancient.'

'Now we're over 40, could you let me drive occasionally?'

'Scuse me, I'm looking for an older woman with experience.'

'Stop saying, "Word on the street" and "My bad". You're a 46-year-old man who lives in a cul-de-sac, whose hobby is gardening and who drinks cocoa before bed-time.'

'I think you look more in your 40s than I do.'

'You're thinking of filling my position with someone younger?!
But I'm only 45!!'

'Oh no! Did I really just say today's pop music is rubbish?!'

'Aagh, my parents have bought me a cardigan.'

'Hope you don't mind me saying so, darling, but you're not the surfer
dude you once were.'

'I thought by my mid-40s I'd have a home, freedom, space, but no,
I'm stuck at my parents' house.'

'Seems our rave days are over. That was Tamsin and Tom
inviting us to a Scrabble night.'

'Groan... it's not the late nights I'm finding difficult;
it's the mornings after.'

'George, quick. Suddenly, I find I'm in my 40s!!
At least tell me I don't look it!'

'Aaaagh! I've just had a nightmare about our mortgage!'

'Ha... I never knew you were hiding a bald patch.'

'I'm in my 40s now. The clock's well and truly ticking.'

'He says he wants stories with more gratuitous violence
like the babysitter tells him.'

'Right, turn off that rubbish you're watching. I've bought a boxset of keep-fit videos for the over-40s.'

'I used to think people in their 40s were ancient.'

'They say life begins at 40, Puss. Hasn't happened to me yet.'

'OK, OK, I know I'm showing my age, but next door's putting rubbish in the wrong bin again.'

'I forget, Tessa. Is it my laser eye treatment or my teeth whitening appointment today?'

'I think I'm having a midlife crisis. I can't stop going to Glastonbury.'

'I know she's sound asleep, but can you check if there's a monster under the bed for me?'

'For my 45th birthday, I'm thinking of buying a new set of golf clubs:
Wentworth, the Belfry, Sunningdale...'

'Do you have anything on your books with a three-mile gravel drive,
croquet lawn and an orangery?'

'Yes, admittedly we're 40 somethings, but very rich 40 somethings!'

'Madame, just think how well this gorgeous Gucci bag would go with your elegance, your age and your bank account.'

'I agree with getting a dog, Nick, but not just any old dog!
Something with a bit of class...'

'Look, Dad, there's your other house.'

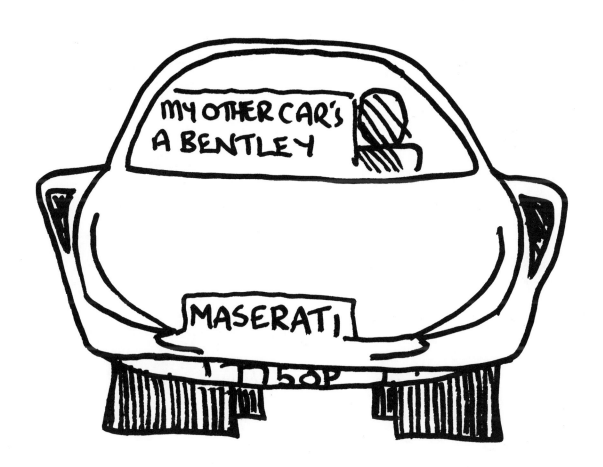

'It's Tim and Julie. They're having a party tonight. If we can't get a babysitter, can I go on my own please?'

'Tequila slammers at our age! Are you sure?'

'All my friends have got kids. But I've got you, Bruno.'

'Fancy forming a middle-aged boy band?'

'Can't remember: is it trendy or not trendy to have a beard?'

'Mummy, mummy, mummy, Jenny at school's mum is in her 40s.
You aren't, are you?'

'She prefers older men... some of them as old as 40.'

'Let's go, Tom. No one here is the right age for us.'

'Hold on there just a minute: I'm only in my 40s. Why would I need life insurance?'

'I've had my first afternoon nap.'

'Of course, we're very proud of your wonderful career, darling, but a tiny part of us is sad we're not blessed with grandchildren.'

'Sorry we're late. He was trying to get into some of his, erm, older trousers.'

'Gasp, I think it's time to take up Crown Green bowling.'

'That was Molly; she's just left me.'

'So he says, "I'm gonna get a tattoo of the love of my life."
I was thinking that's really sweet of him, but now he's gone and got
"UNITED" printed across his back.'

'Your jeans are too tight; your face has gone blue.'

'You should get your wife to shave your back like I do, mate.'

'Aaagh! Nose hairs!'

'Great news, I'm resurrecting my old vinyl collection!'

'For goodness sake, will someone please ask her how the teeth whitening went?'

'I'm not sure I've successfully made the leap
from my 30s to my 40s.'

'OK, listen. Our Joe's split up with Debbie. She's keeping the flat and he's moving back in with us. Isn't that great?'

'Dear Mum and Dad, don't worry about me. I've got a couple of lovely friends.'

'I've reached an age where I could have a toy boy.'

'Son, are you going to be OK in a flat on your own? You're only 41.'

'Turn that music down. Aaagh! Sorry, son, forget it.
I'm sounding like my dad.'

'Oh no, I just looked in the bathroom mirror and saw my dad staring back at me.'

'Funny how *we're* drawn more to the wines these days.'

'Sorry we're late. We were just watching Peppa Pig with the kids.'

'The older I get, the more I look like the dog.'

'This is my school diary: "Prediction -- by my 45th birthday I will have walked on the Moon."'

'As I get older, I seem to spend more and more time at your surgery. My wife thinks we're having an affair.'

'I imagine being a single mum in your 40s is much harder.'

'Psst... anti-wrinkle cream, please.'

'43 and just been asked for ID... Get in there!'

'No way, you're never in your 40s.'

'Dad, you're in your 40s now. Don't you think you should be cutting down on the wine?'

'I'm not giving in to this age thing. Gasp!'

'We had a choice, children or dogs. We chose the latter.'

'What do you mean, no over-35s?'

'Do you remember when we used to go out to enjoy ourselves?'